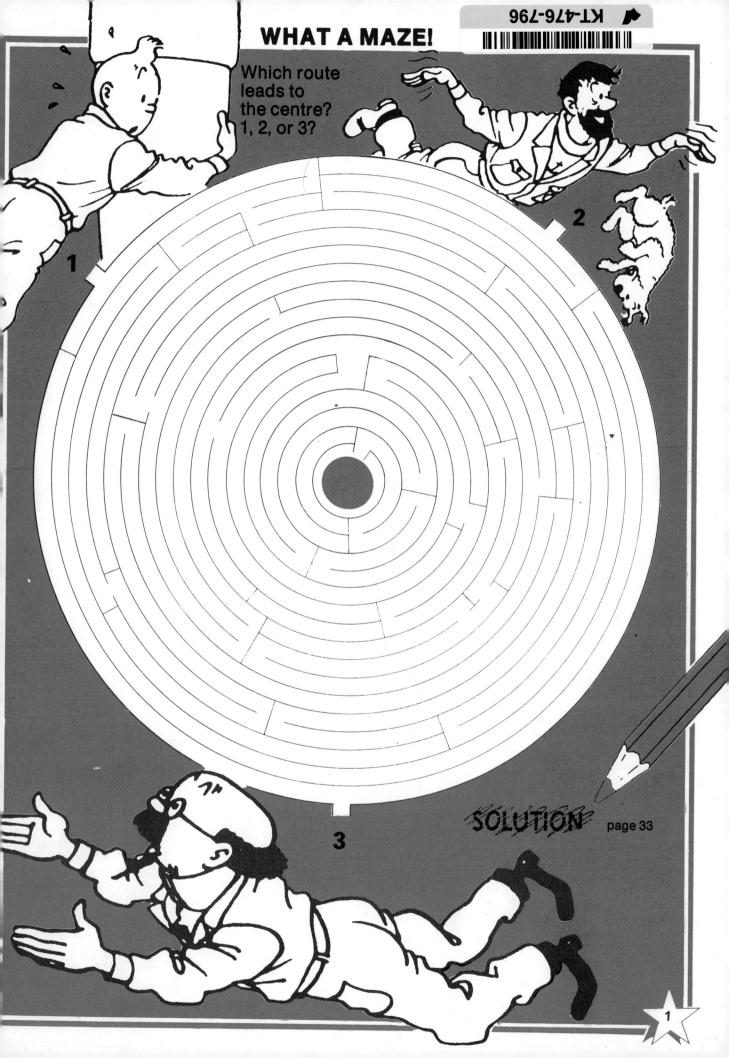

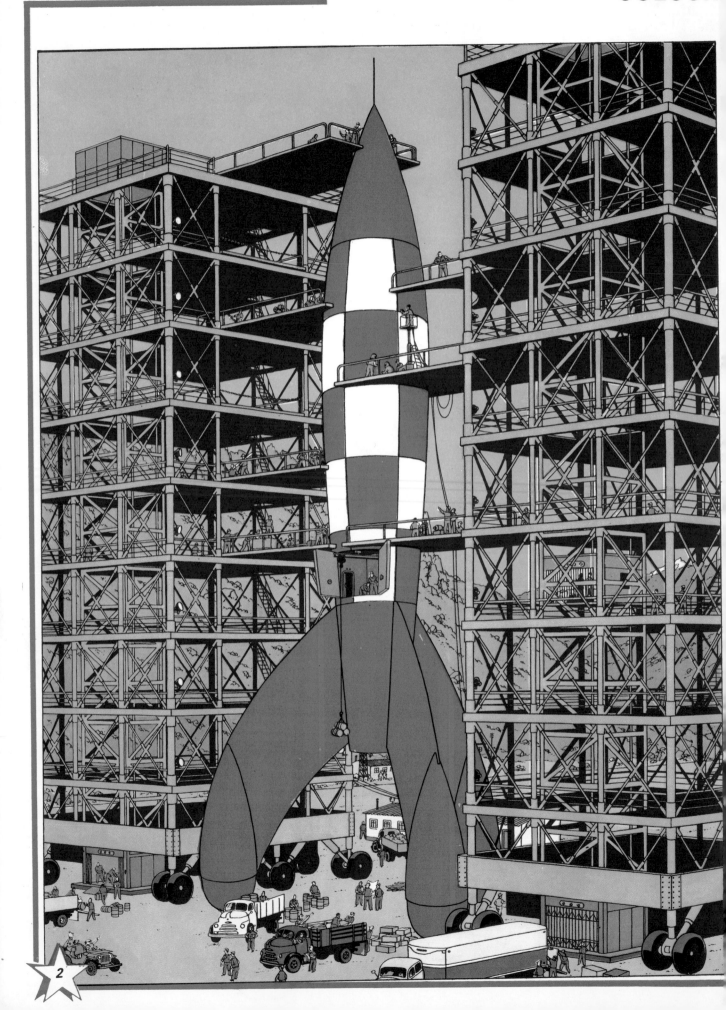

AND DISCOVER

Colour this picture, compare with the opposite page, and discover 7 mistakes.

TWINS

These patterns
are paired –
with one exception!

Which is the
odd one out?

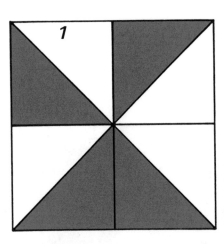

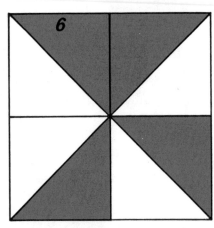

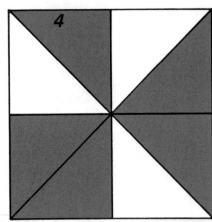

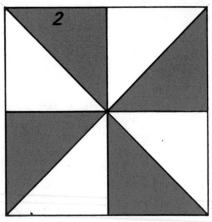

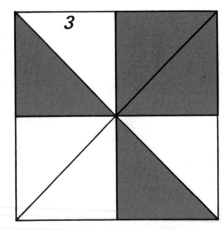

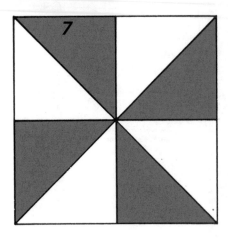

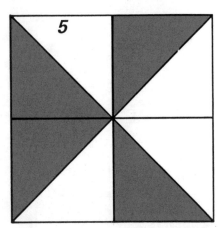

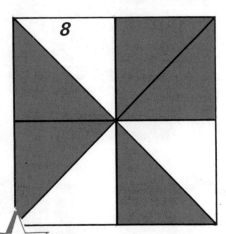

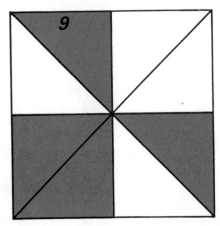

SOLUTION   page 33

DESTINATION MOON

left in ... to rejoin ... in Syldavia. There ... asked ... and ... to go to the moon with him.

Our friends ... and the ... , and a surprise visit by

The ... tested the weight of his

From being very timid ... becomes

but he ... and loses his memory.

Disguised as a ... , a ... , the

helps ... to recover by giving him a fright. The

Technicians track the rocket by ...

"Hello! Hello! – Earth calling . . . Earth calling Lunar Rocket. . . " There was no answer.

Have no fear for our friends, their adventures will continue!

For the present they have just gone for a walk on the moon!

5

Using his binoculars, the Professor can see exactly what our friends are doing on the moon.

SPOT

Can you identify which parts of the lunar scene have been 'spotted' by the Professor?

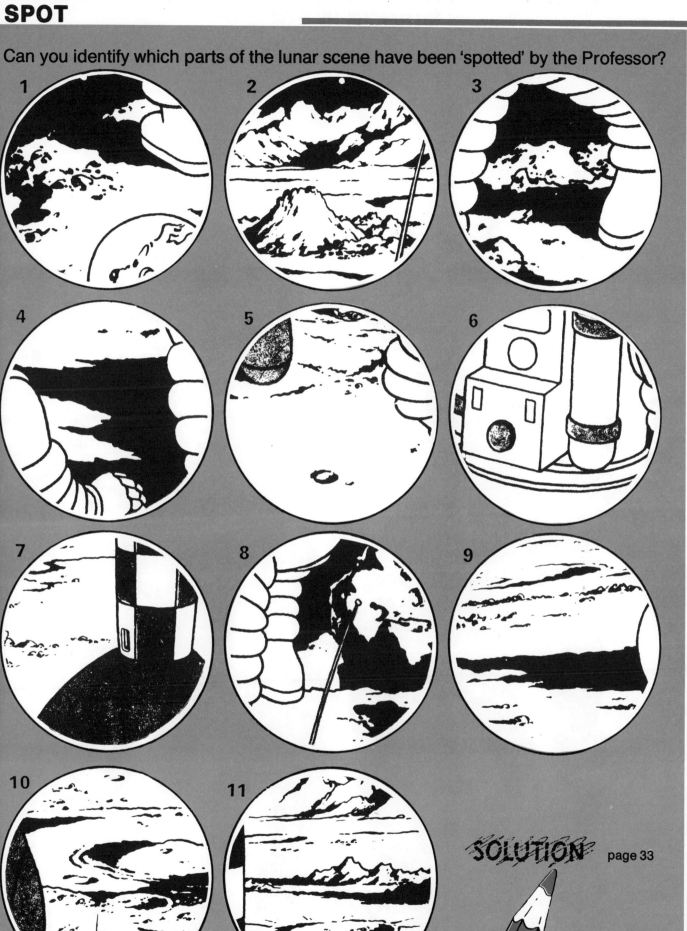

SOLUTION page 33

7

MIRROR IMAGE?

These drawings are almost identical,
but there is an error in the picture on the right.

What is it?

SOLUTION page 33

CUT UP AND REASSEMBLE

What is the message?

SOLUTION page 33

How many . . .
black stars
yellow stars
and question marks
can you see?

10

DON'T PANIC!

SOLUTION   page 33

11

ARE THESE IDENTICAL?

No! There are 7 mistakes in the bottom picture. Can you find them?

12

DOT TO DOT

What are Captain Haddock, Professor Calculus and Tintin looking at?
Hurry! Join up the dots from 1 to 84 and find out.

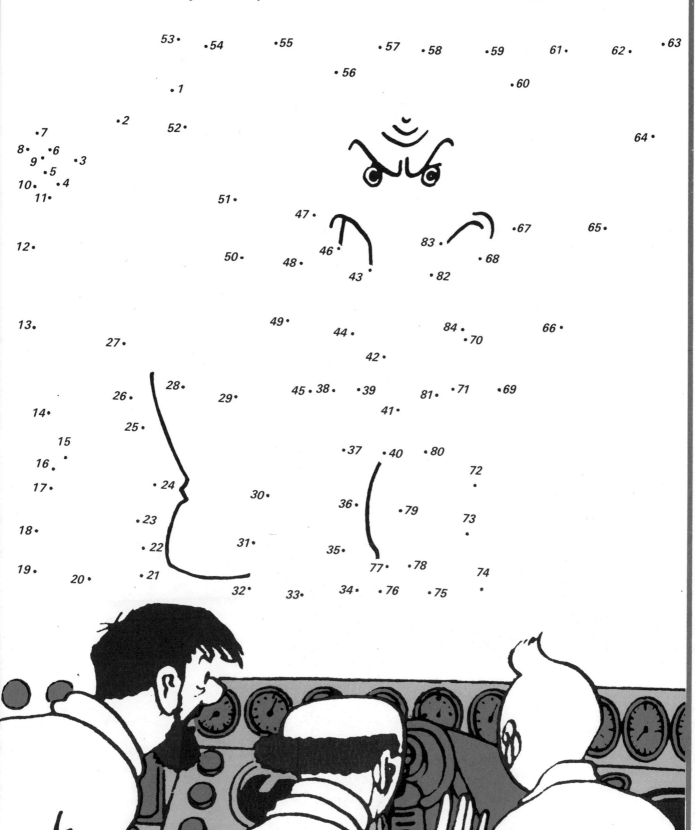

1 It fires a ball
2 Sea bird that feeds on fish
3 Controls the navigation of a ship
4 This will save a drowning man
5 Small boat
6 This is propelled by wind

7 Made of wood or metal it carries the sails
8 Made of wood and held between the teeth
9 Master of a ship
10 Seamen who raid and plunder
11 Dropped when a ship docks

CROSSWORD

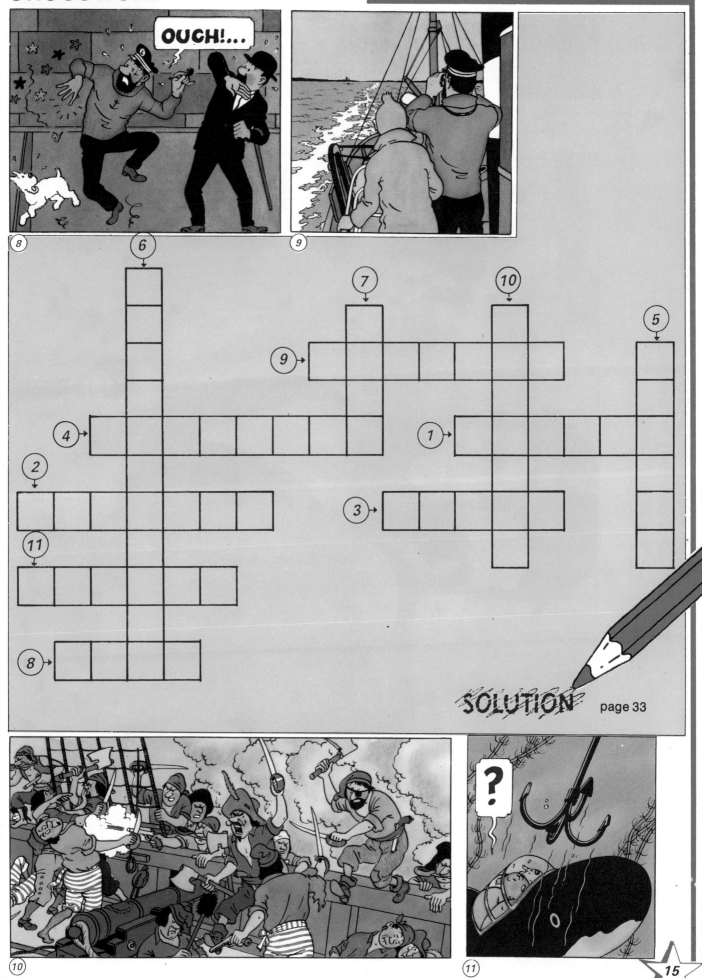

OUCH!...

SOLUTION page 33

15

SOMETHING WRONG?

There are 10 things wrong in this picture.
Can you find them?

SOLUTION page 33

16

SPACE TO DRAW

Use the grid to reproduce
Professor Calculus's face.

SEARCH AND FIND

With the help of his telescope, the Captain can see details on the ships.

Can you identify the parts he is looking at?

SOLUTION page 33

Which of these rockets comes from earth?

WHICH?

Which dagger will reach the centre of the red target?

A ruler will help you to decide.

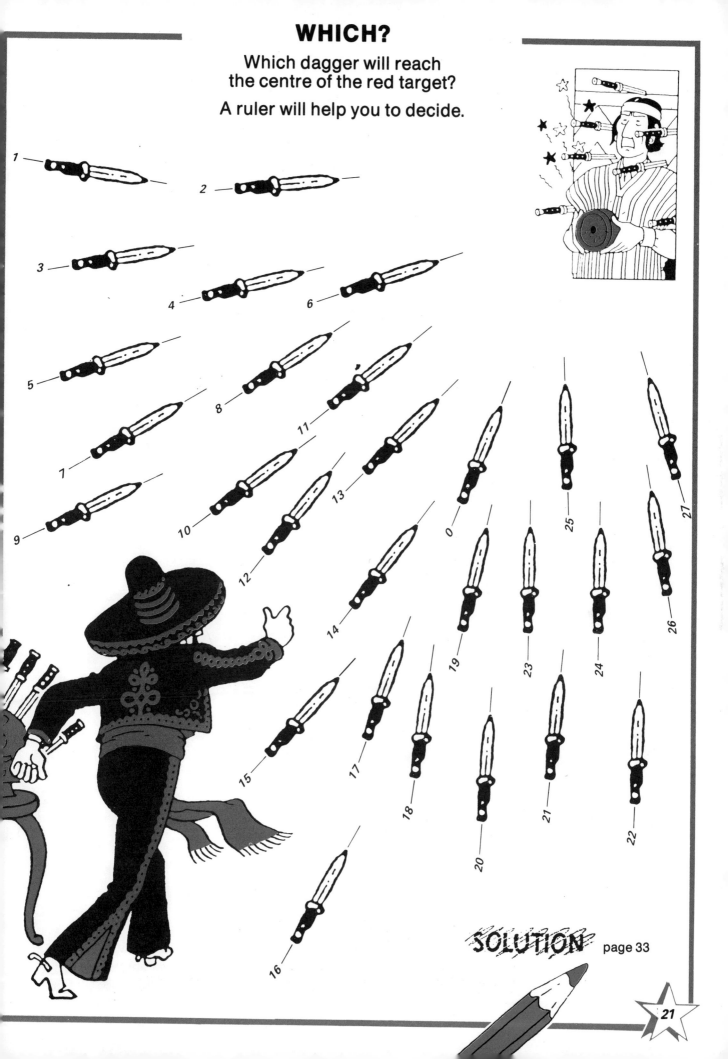

SOLUTION page 33

COLOUR

and colour this figure on the grid.

Each aeroplane and
vehicle appears twice.
But one
aeroplane

OUT

and one car do not!

Which are they?

SOLUTION page 33

A LABYRINTH

Which route will the firemen take to rejoin their fire engine?

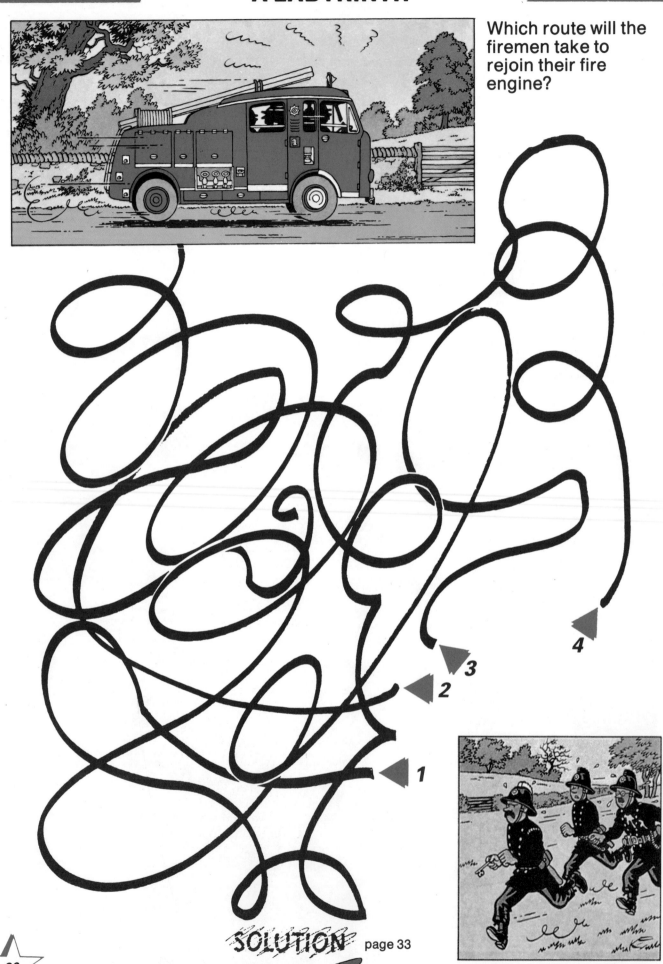

SOLUTION page 33

SHADOW PLAY

Tintin is afraid of the big dragon. One of the little dragon shadows is identical with the big dragon. Which one?

SOLUTION page 33

Where do these people come from?

N. A_ _ _ _ _ _

C_ _ _ _ _

M_ _ _ _ _

A_ _ _ _ _ _

G_ _ _ _ _

S_ _ _ _ _ _ _ _

P_ _ _

SOLUTION page 33

LIFT THESE!

Sort the dumb-bells in order from smallest
to largest and enter the numbers in these boxes.

SOLUTION page 33

COLOUR THIS IN

A DIFFERENCE

One Thompson is different from the others. Which one?

STICKING PLASTER

Look carefully and put each of these scenes in their correct order.
The first scene is number 2.
Write the numbers in order in these boxes.

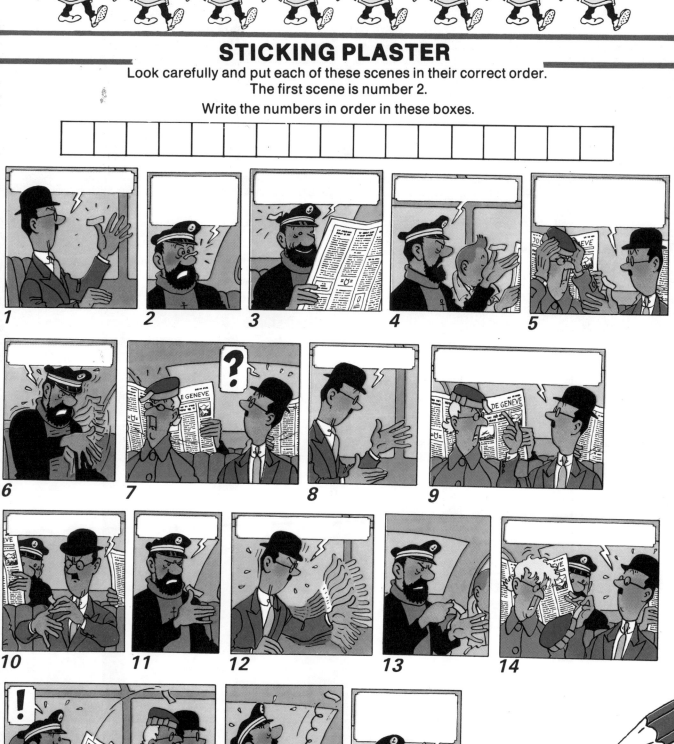

SOLUTION page 33

THOMPSON AND THOMSON

One of these pictures of Thompson (or Thomson) is repeated twice. Which one?

32

MAGICAL SOLUTIONS

Use a soft pencil to reveal the hidden answers!

A GAME OF HIDDEN MAGIC

A game for 2 players with pencils, each taking a turn.

The first player has the choice of the Professor or Tintin with the corresponding play panel. Play starts in the top group of boxes and continues down in horizontal lines.

To move, the player must scribble over one box at a time. If the champion's head is revealed, the player may scribble over a 2nd box in the next horizontal line – and so on until the final line of boxes.

If a player fails to reveal an occupied box he or she must remain in the same line of boxes.

The first player to reveal all 9 'heads' is the winner.